Contents

0.0
Sharpen
By Rich Ives
Illustrations by Jack Callil
Diagrams by Nils Davey

This manual is for Sharpen
Model-V12014 only.

9 780989 092678

For further information go to
theNewerYork.com/sharpen

Bench Clamp
/benCH/klamp/

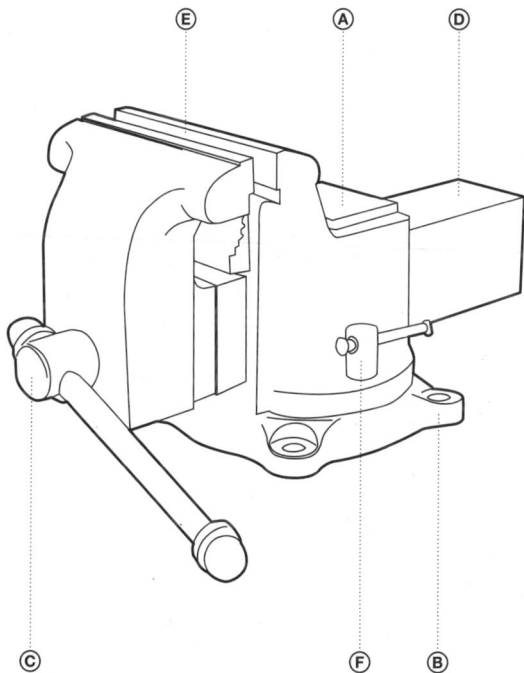

1.1
A bench clamp
(A) is used to hold
an object in place
on a workbench
using inward
pressure. It is
typically flush with
the work surface
(B). The handle (C)
rotates, moving
the slide (D), which
in turn moves
the dynamic jaw
closer or farther
from the static
jaw (E).

Chapter 1   The tongue of the knife moves in and out of its calling, speaking of separations and what's necessary. What a daughter says can be held longer in the weight of its own compression. Its teeth are merely texture. Something large is held to something small by the weight of the consideration.

It almost tickles where you can't scratch it, desire too long restrained. I can tell. I can almost feel my daughter squirming with it.

Both of us hold on to our adjustments and tune them to the modifications we have learned. Jaws then, jaws of there was no one to release me. Jaws of waiting. Jaws of impatience without intention. A body telling you to operate, to function, to be a body, to say it. Suddenly the body is yours. It holds you together. It has much more to say. I remember that.

Then it's said, and it can't be removed. It doesn't matter much what it is because they're all alike. They're all sharp and appear unexpectedly though it must have been carried a long time, that thing she said. Time is ours again, but the words aren't. We're both holding on to it, observing it, trying to understand why it's fastened there between us, sharp and gleaming, impatient. There's no more illusion, which isn't so bad, but we don't know what to do without it, so we stand there, not looking at each other, looking at what was said, which hangs between us and seems invisible but isn't because what it can receive has been sharpened.

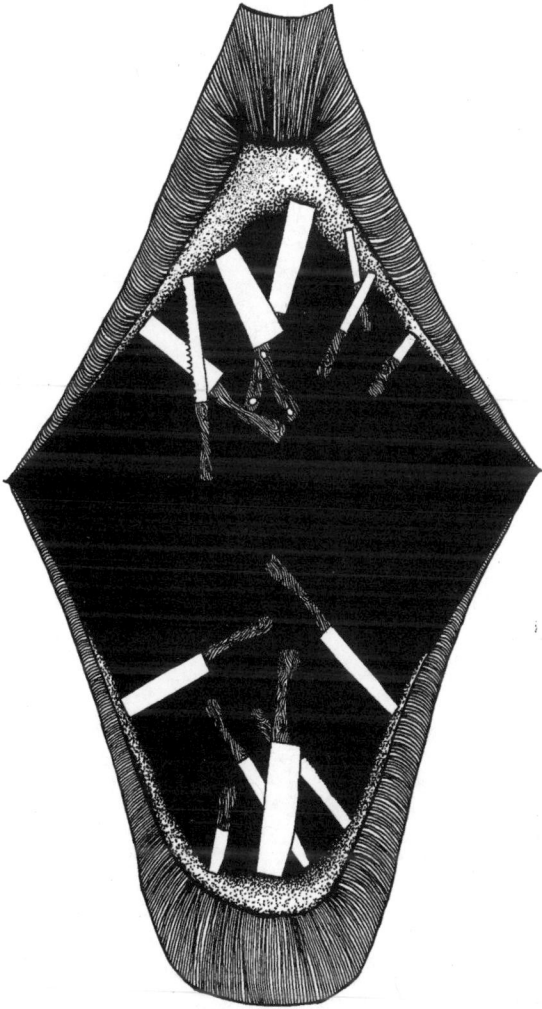

1.2
First locate an anchor with metal jaws. Hardware stores attract the mouth only, not yet attached to the body. Drag one home and attach at the corner of your chosen bench. Rotate the imprisoned baton handle until the jaws open. This will be a collaboration. Insert your project and tighten the jaws.

Lactation Dance

/lak'tāSH(ə)n/dans/

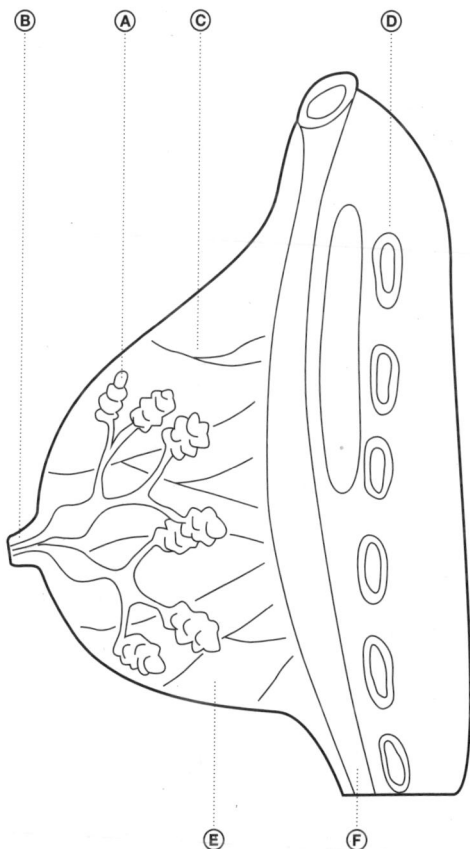

2.1
Lactation is the secretion of milk from the mammary glands. It is also used to refer to the period of time during which milk is produced by female mammals. The lobules (A) excrete milk toward the nipple (B). Milk is an opaque, white fluid, rich in fat and protein, which provides the primary nourishment necessary for young mammals to thrive.

Chapter 2   Listen, Snow Geese, you have no right falling upon stubbled fields, confusing snow as if you were the ghostly breasts and the bearded fields could welcome you more than they could a baby.

The night merely painted on and fluttering down to collect emotional taxes, spending darkness as it goes. It's not the one arrived at who waits patiently. It's a gift, this arriving at the next, a gift I don't know what to do with.

As with a heart of milk, or a vinegar intention, a regression too gets released, as the heads of babies are placed there, in your empty hands, their allegations too unsupported to even deny.

We've used up the abuse of circumstance now, and we have to sample our intentions.

Appears to share only inconsequential arrivals with the departed. Sits with uncertainty quietly as if it might break.

She does not know she is the Snow Geese, the daughter of my daughter, or the right to be falling, or the stubbled fields still confusing snow and ghostly breath. She does not know beards yet, or even babies, not even this one, which can be true again and again, but already she is leaking.

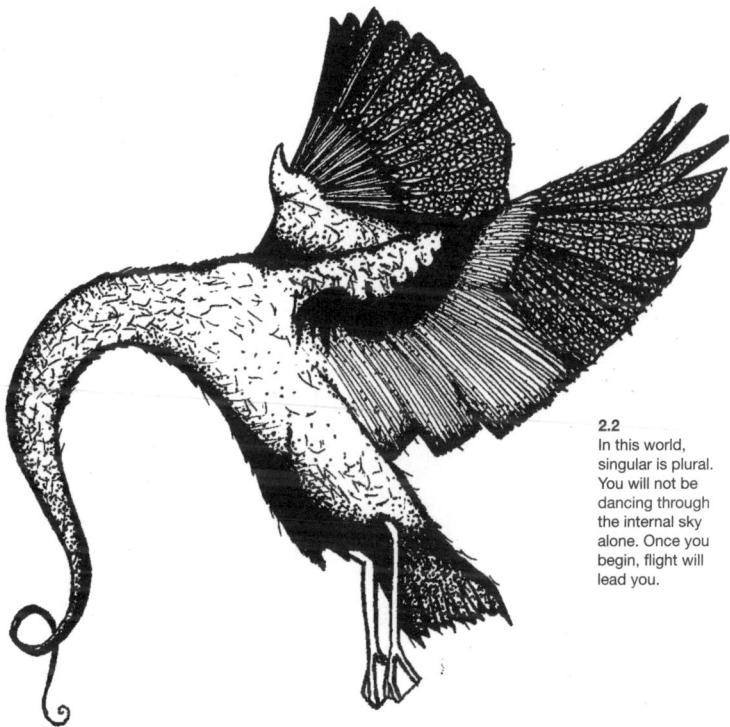

2.2
In this world, singular is plural. You will not be dancing through the internal sky alone. Once you begin, flight will lead you.

Witchet
/wiCHət/

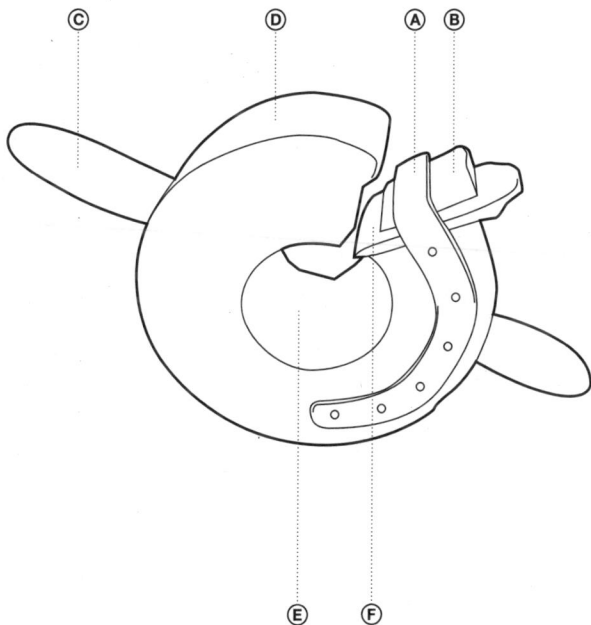

3.1
Also known
as a rounding
plane, the
witchet is usually
constructed of
wood, though
it may have
reinforcements of
brass and steel
(A and B). Correct
usage results in a
rounding cut that
can be tapered by
manipulating the
threaded arms (C).
It is used to shape
wooden and metal
dowels for use
as tool handles.
Widget may be a
corruption of the
word witchet.

Chapter 3   *This ring can be worn but once,* says the forlorn daughter's dream. The fingers are wooden, unnaturally straight knuckles diced smooth and worn. You might think she was a puppet if she weren't talking about love though there is no one here to listen. Except me, of course, and she doesn't realize I'm listening. I'm outside her space, outside her current sadness.

That's not a stack of dried browned rainbows but dowels I've fashioned, to hold things between this and that in my daughter's space, between here and there, between cared for and fallen. It seems we've both been away. It seems we have more important things to do, but of course we do not. That's why we are observing the negligence so carefully.

Over the sour breath of the radiator, there's a faint oyster smell edged with rust and burnt metal. A child's decaled lampshade seems abandoned in the corner, perched uneasily on a dusty stool. It drops its sepia cowboys like leaves. The new bulb was too bright for old children's dreams. They curled off and fell.

Nobody's speaking in the dream any more. No one says what this is about, but you can flatten it and read it slowly as the words gallop off, or hang it on a towel rack until somebody wishes to use it again and forgets how it has already failed to produce the desired result.

You can glue one of the dowels upright and slide the ring over it, as if it's only the first of many childish marriages. A daughter can try again. Can a father?

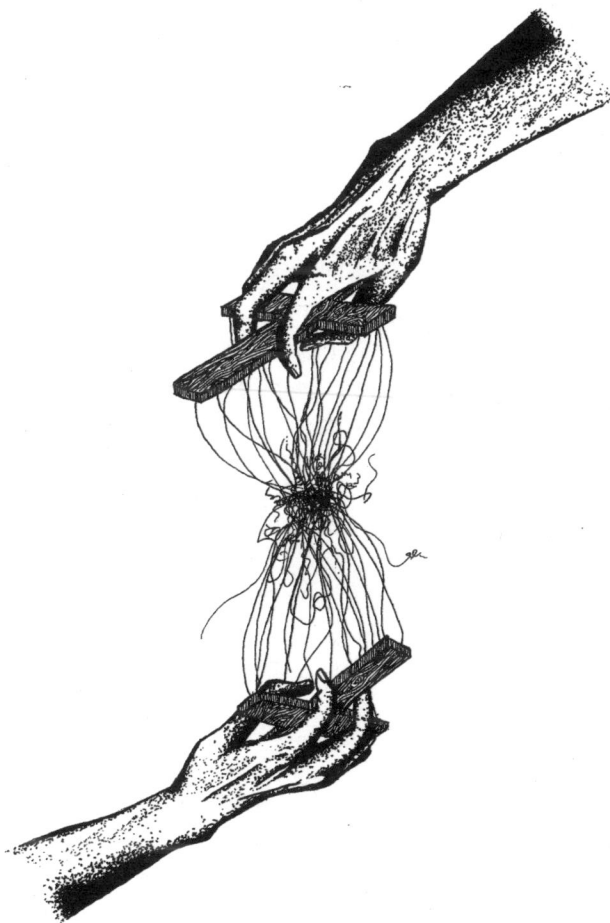

3.2
Intense and self-reflective, they dance lightly and appear to link the past with the future. They easily fray and contain rogue threads of what might appear to be rebellion but actually shape the cohesive structure of the puppets' silent speech. The birch trees that birthed them provide the anchors.

Whetstone
/ˈ(h)wetˌstōn/

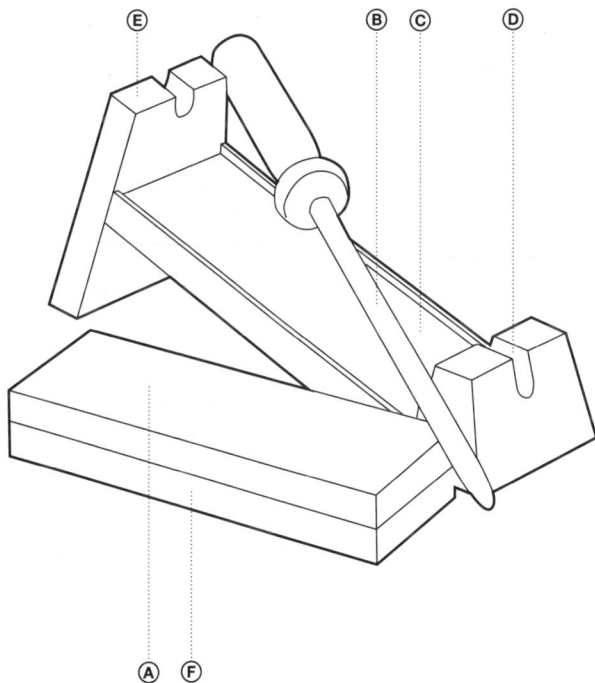

4.1
Whetstones
(or sharpening
stones) are fine-
grained stones (A)
used to sharpen
the edges of steel
tools, weapons,
and implements.
They may be
flat or shaped,
quarried, or man-
made. Sharpening
with a whetstone
is sometimes
called "stoning."

Chapter 4   I wanted to enter and leave with very little, the remainder more itself, more its purpose, identifiable by its smoothness in the wake of abrasion, but this was before, and Spring says yes to Spring the way the sky falls and then opens when happiness begins spilling, but this too was before.

The stain of the captain's bleeding tobacco when he was with the woman and only had love to choose from, when the wings of mosquitoes occupied his imagination, when he was unable to attend to the dissection of his thinking, when collision is symptom of not once but twice, and this too was before.

A faded orange dress appears to have rubbed partially off, turning with a body against itself, just a little less than, just before the key change when we began singing, the hunched dowager risen before the strike, before we were singing. No dogs to chase us and the husband is hungry. That's what she thinks, rising to the occasion of the singing, but that too was before.

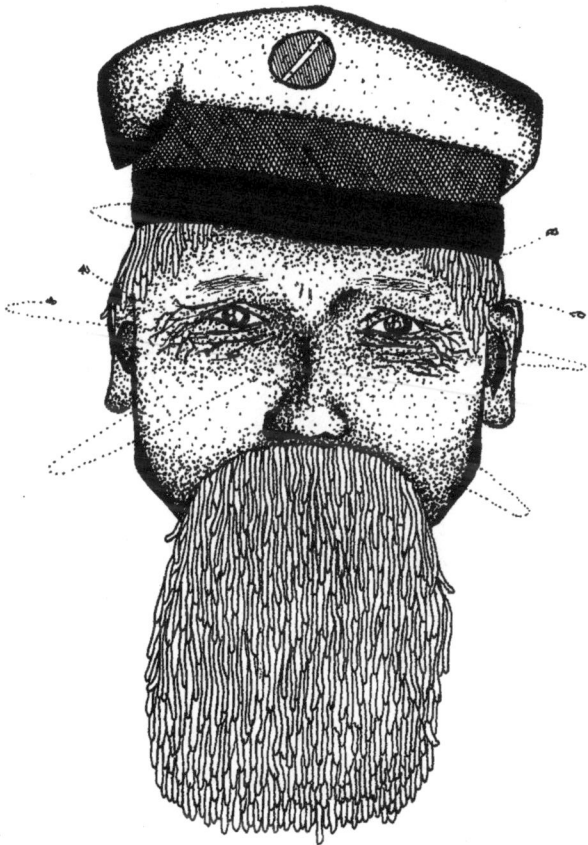

4.2
Now you must release the unnecessary, which falls away in soft lengthy clumps of thick hair-like words.

Grindstone
/ˈgrīndˌstōn/

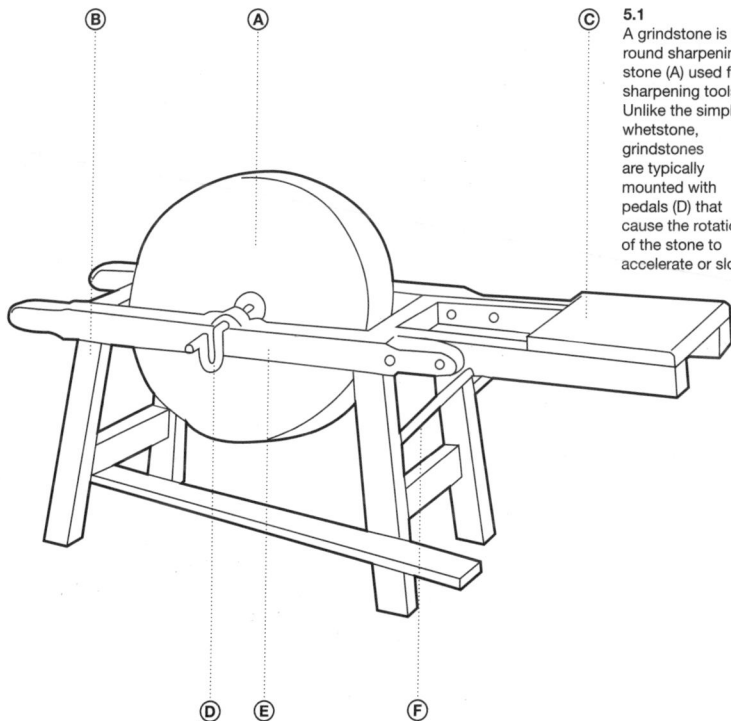

5.1
A grindstone is a round sharpening stone (A) used for sharpening tools. Unlike the simpler whetstone, grindstones are typically mounted with pedals (D) that cause the rotation of the stone to accelerate or slow.

Chapter 5   I can't seem to relate to cloud cover. Take it down, where
a shepherd's crook is performing vaudevillian removals in
such tiny increments that rejection looks like acceptance.

Take it down. The winds confuse themselves and part
the clouds with parts of the clouds. They reassemble the
space behind the blade of their own being. Take it down.

I believe I'm gamely, but blame assimilates the bleed. I'm
responsible for the selection of leftovers. Drink to me only
with thine I's. An impressionist made the coffee grinder.
I'm deliciously compromised. Take it down.

The landing gear of nicks and scratches catches and falls
away until only water will accept us. Take it down.

Leather it out then with stout strokes of sliding to separate
perfection from perception. Not until the stroke collects
its donation do we know the gift.

5.2
The egg you will
use to descend
from the watery
sky should
be dark and
cushioned within
your more obvious
intentions.

The Inner Ear

/ˈinər/i(ə)r/

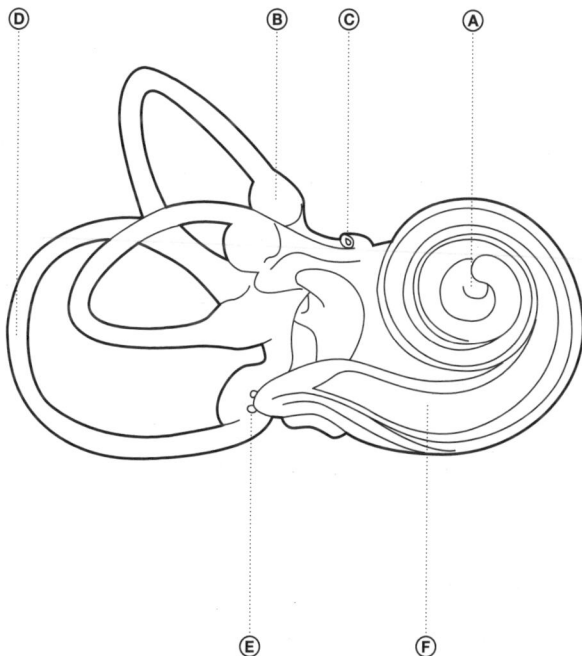

6.1
The inner ear is used for sound detection and balance. The cochlea (A) converts sound pressure patterns into electrochemical impulses that are then passed to the brain through the auditory nerve. The vestibular system (B, D) sends signals that control eye movements and keep a creature upright. Though found in all vertebrates, there are substantial variations in form and function.

Chapter 6   It was a night of owls, like this one. Deep in summer. I could hear them calling me to what I had hoped for my daughter, to the life inside and the far hopes at once.

Dreams were separating themselves from the impossible. I was experiencing my own creation. As if I had lived previously only on my balcony.

I could hear something translated from that other life, the one where I fathered my intelligence, my feelings, set them free. Before that I had been an explosion of containment. I withheld, violently.

I remembered having two parents. I remembered a childhood, but most of the details escaped me. Not hidden. Not denied. Just ordinary. Unworthy of mention. Lawn chairs can hold a less limited life. The canvas contained no color worthy of repeating. Something wonderful and complex hadn't even begun yet.

But they were only details, those realities. Nothing could live up to what I imagined, and as long as I could keep on imagining, that was the way I wanted it.

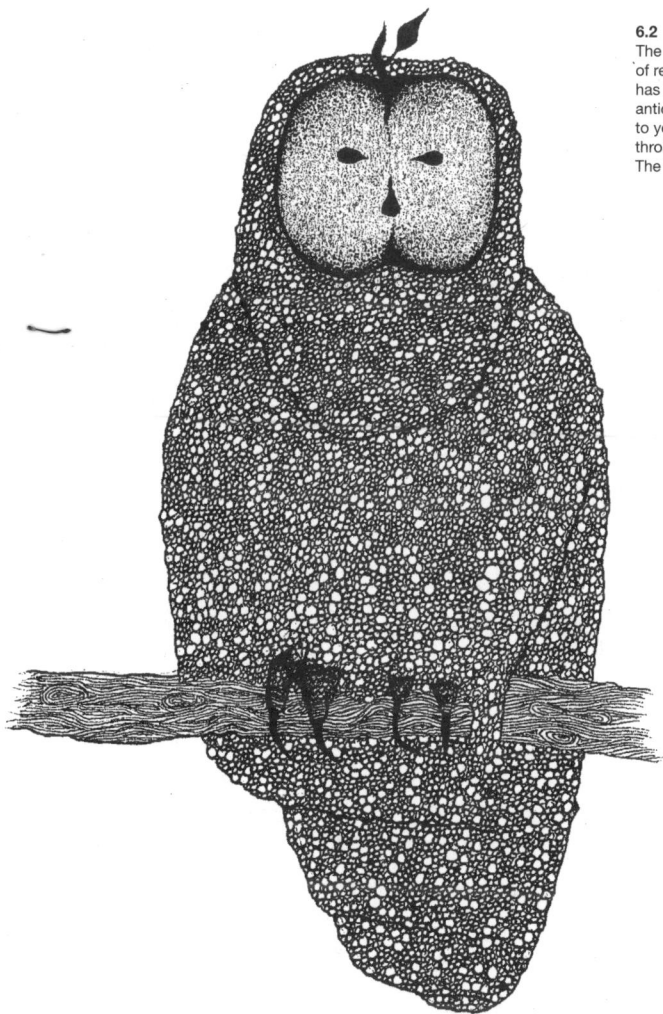

6.2
The vast ocean
of release
has brought
anticipation
to your softly
throbbing head.
The forest awaits.

Vise

/vīs/

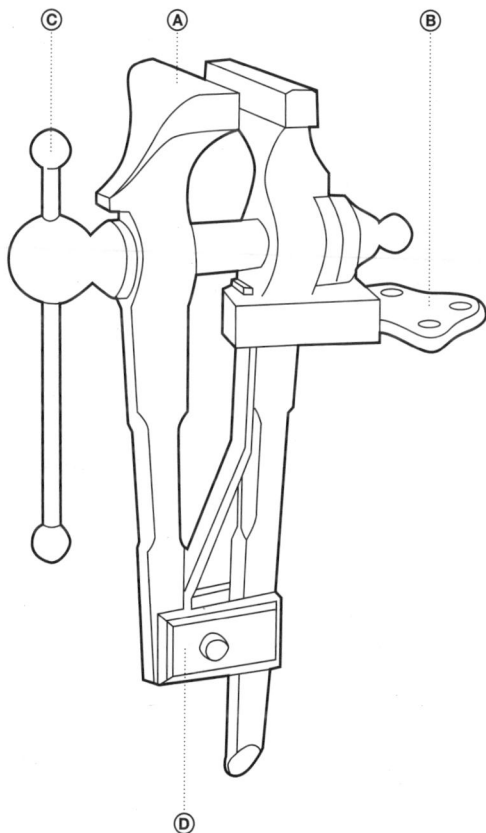

7.1
A metalworking vise is made of cast steel, featuring jaws (A) that are separate and replaceable, usually engraved with serrated or raw diamond-like teeth. Soft jaw covers made of aluminum or lead may be used to protect delicate work. Also known as an engineer's vise, it is sometimes bolted to the top surface of a workbench (B).

Chapter 7   I was pressed tight against a private entrance and squeezed until the juice bled. The small wall of a room made from connecting one uncertainty to another needed the support of something I didn't understand. Neither did my daughter or my granddaughter, I'm sure, but they suffered from it in their own ways.

Leave, until the foreign feels familiar. That was the principle. A new country will never cross again my own tightly bound border, not even when it breaks. That's what I thought. The other country wishes to remain the other country.

We could never understand this, all my daughters and I, because the characters were hidden dimensions of us, just as we were dimensions, sometimes hidden, of ourselves. We were beasts at the edges of each other. We poked and prodded to see what dangers lay there, waiting to attach themselves.

By the time that cave had become a discarded character of its own, questionable characters had appeared around the corners of newly arrived buildings of more recent imagination. The questionable characters limited the buildings but not the questionable characters. It was a way of uniting cause and effect that helped us understand what we were a part of. After that we let go.

7.2
This is the
most patient
illumination of
your project. Have
you forgotten you
are composed of
devices?

8.0

C Clamp
/sē/klamp/

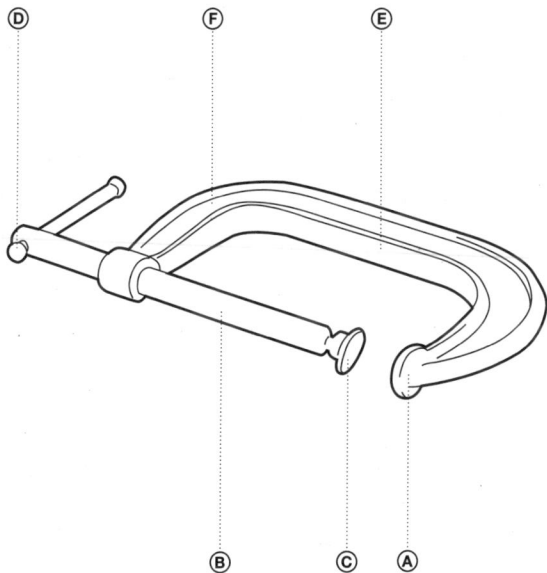

8.1
A C clamp is typically made of steel or cast iron. It includes a small flat edge (A) and a threaded hole which contains a screw (B) with another flat edge (C). The c clamp has a small resistant bar (D), perpendicular to the screw itself, which is used to gain leverage when tightening the clamp. When the clamp is completely closed, the flat end of the screw comes into contact with the flat end of the frame (E).

Chapter 8   Between one touch and another touch, there is holding onto ourselves through another. I'm saying this because someone must have a reason. Someone must have something in mind, if mind is the intention and holding on to is the intermediate result.

I lived on crumbs, but the crumbled did not become me. I was held by the fingers of a deliberate prod, turned and turned to put me together with myself and cut away the excess. For this I held very still.

I read to myself from the book of self. I did this while my daughter was sleeping. Sometimes I watched her sleep, but it usually led me to reading. That kind of reading did not appear in a book, but I read it, and I lined the words up that described what I was doing. They were my words. I understood them differently when I read them than when I put them together. I lined up the soldiers of their lost war, and I shot them full of the holes I was trying to fill. I wanted them to execute me. For this I waited.

Sometimes I seem to surprise ourselves with the tools I can apply between one finger and another. Do I really line up? Do I hold still long enough? Do I stand too close to see clearly, to operate effectively the tools of this exchange?

If you have no father, what you say is a father, teaching you to behave this way, just this way, its spores the tyrant pollens of a falling sky, a habit of distress multiplying, one of the skies of sex bursting.

Let the part of you that eats be eaten. Hold this between your longer thin fingers, and do not diminish yourself. Wait for the operation you want another, who is more capable, to perform.

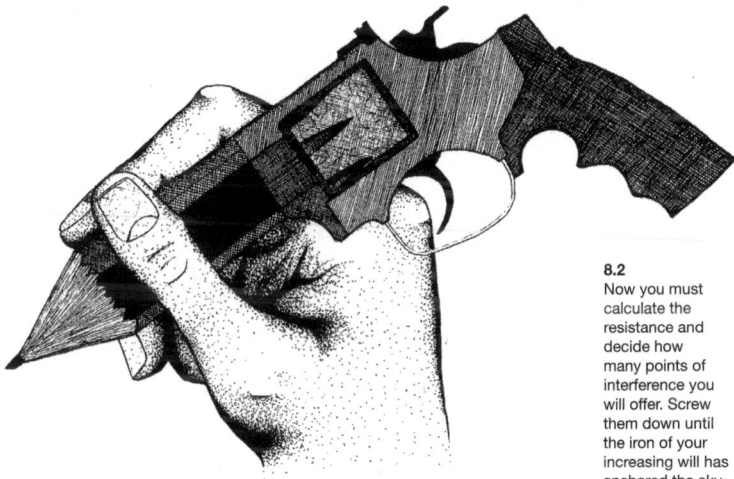

8.2
Now you must calculate the resistance and decide how many points of interference you will offer. Screw them down until the iron of your increasing will has anchored the sky upon the table with the ocean contained inside it.

Ghost Twins

/gōst/twinz/

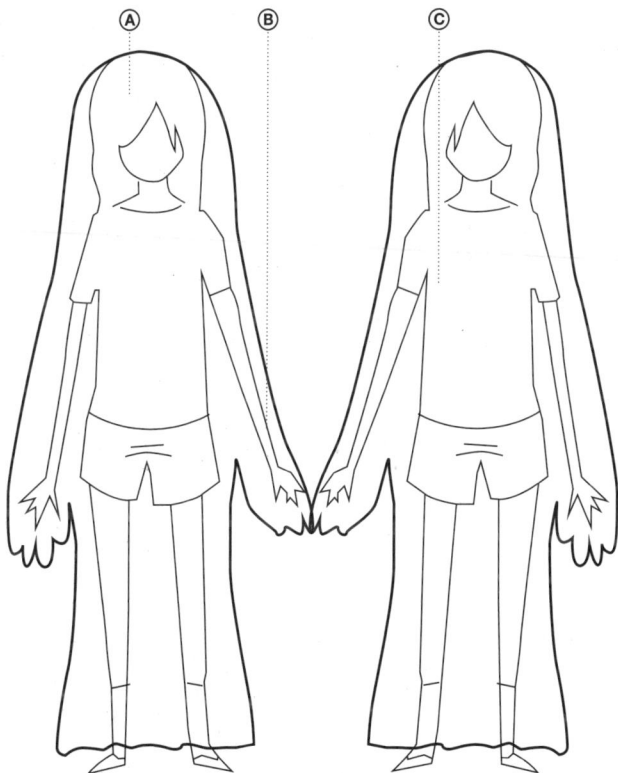

Ⓐ   Ⓑ   Ⓒ

9.1

In traditional belief and fiction, a ghost is the undeparted spirit of a deceased person or animal that can appear, visibly or invisibly, to the living. Descriptions of these apparitions vary widely, from an invisible presence to a translucent or barely visible shape (A), or even a more lifelike vision that contains some aberration.

Chapter 9   Dulled dear daughter lights up the mother, lights up two of
everything, two ones and two others, two nervous wrens
of gray light moving in the shape of the one gone. Time
is a love poem intricately woven into different pacings,
marked equidistantly on the heart's projected eye. As if
one could see the other's attachments objectively.

Here, a door passes between rooms as if it could not stop
coming and going, as if the room were not defined by its
presence.

A window is always open to interpretation. Which side are
you on? The one that must disassemble and fall through?
The one that has already fallen backwards, into itself,
from the darkness?

I am the room. I am the doorway. I am the box within the
room. I am everything my ghost daughters are not. That is
how I can remain inside the room with myself. What's the
gender of this lament?

Light pouring in through an open window closes the
darkness, thinking into the corners, where it meets itself
and lingers, not recognizing yet where it's going.

Light pours in through the uncertainty we must live in.
The barefoot suffering of the abstracted runner arrives
before the runner does. Unencumbered by intentions, it
finds itself everywhere, as if everywhere were a singular
destination, as if everywhere were here.

This is only attentive, not attended, sensitive, not sensed.
This is the gesture without the gesturer. This is the
moment without its cause. This clown walking sideways

is not me, but my possibility. Is that really me, not me laughing behind a face that does?

A blue arabesque, the daughter who meets your eyes, the one whose throat is too slender to swallow anything as distasteful as fate.

How do you perform without a mouth, without a tongue, without anything inside that can be seen? What do you say with the part of you that survived, when fly is not the word that comes to the bird, silently?

A daughter places that winged creature in the father's hand, or the mother does, before the daughter arrives, but only what the father offers contains the rest of the desired sky, releasing.

9.2
The twins may
not reveal their
purpose easily
for they too are
singular, the dance
of daughters
so very polite
and measured.
They are not at
rest, there inside
your head with
the mother, who
has initiated
this project with
her absence.
The window is
open. Where
is the unified
perception? You
will miss me now.
You will assemble
the parts.

Rich Ives
The Author

10.1
Rich Ives may have first been sighted by a gossipy albino fox near a northeastern South Dakota cabbage patch of questionable lineage with his thirteen wives, each of whom inexplicably disappeared into the neighboring and not yet Monsanto-ghosted cornfield. As a result, his relatives have mostly given up on him, and yet he remains relative. Rich Ives may actually be a euphemism for a pervasive bearded pollen preferred for cocoon sealing by the Gypsy Moth when overwintering beyond its normal habitat. Rich Ives has no normal habitat, but still he seems to overwinter in a log home despite reports of a great spewing infestation of threads of words and music. The cocoon appears to have as many as three doors through which he enters and exits frequently with these gentle-winged sermons. Why must he explain himself so often when he could be comfortably making himself up?

Jack Callil
The Illustrator

My name is Jack Callil and I'm quite an incredible person. I'm witty, and have had people tell me on more than one occasion that I smell particularly well scented (A) and I'd have to agree with them on that. I can grow a nice full face of stubble (B), and quite pride myself on the size of my adams apple (C) – I've yet to find another which matches mine in prodigiousness. My laugh is well regulated, doesn't range too high in pitch or volume, and have found it's most suited to jokes and when someone falls over. I have an incredible birthmark, but it's under my hair (D) and I've never seen it. I enjoy pasta.